INTRODUCTION

This is the second of the series of starting points for mathematical investigations and like its predecessor this pamphlet draws on the experience of many teachers and makes no claim to originality.

Points of Departure has attracted a great deal of interest and we have heard that in addition to meeting the original need for starting points for children's mathematical investigations, the pamphlet has been widely used for the mathematical development of teachers on in-service courses. We hope that Points of Departure 2 will prove equally valuable.

Our thanks are due to those who have contributed ideas for this pamphlet and we extend an invitation to you to send material for further publications to the ATM Office.

TANSY HARDY   ANNE HAWORTH   ERIC LOVE

LIST OF STARTING POINTS

1. Rectangle Areas
2. Halving the Board
3. Number Cells
4. Cutcake
5. Taking Counters
6. Polyominoes and Symmetry
7. Strips of Squares
8. Two-piece Tangrams
9. Palindromic Dates
10. Polygon Symmetries
11. Lines and Regions
12. Slices
13. Tessellating Hexiamonds
14. Transforming Numbers
15. Speedway Heats
16. Matrix Powers
17. Patio Tiles
18. Round the Block
19. Near to the Root
20. Calendars

21. Cuboids
22. Noughts and Crosses
23. Drawing Squares
24. Quadrant Tiles
25. Maximum Cone
26. Dotty Shapes
27. Polygons within Polygons 1
28. Polygons within Polygons 2
29. Number Spirals
30. Tables
31. Hiccup Numbers
32. Stamps
33. Maximum Area
34. Joining Dots
35. Adding Digits
36. Monge's Shuffle
37. Breaking Sticks
38. Moving Arrowheads
39. Airline Luggage
40. Tessellating Pentominoes
41. Pegboard Arrays

42. Nodes
43. Maxagon
44. Projections
45. African Network Patterns
46. Crossing Hexagons
47. Finding Triangles
48. Patience
49. Babytags
50. Squaring Matrices
51. Broom and Band
52. Isometric Transformations
53. Mod 5 Transformations
54. Bell Ringing
55. Binary Ones
56. Elephant Walk
57. Frogs
58. Folding Stamps
59. Enclosures
60. Dotty Variations
61. Transforming Triangles

1. RECTANGLE AREAS

Use squared paper

Here are some rectangles of area 10 square units

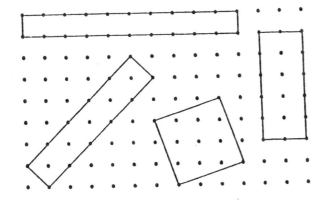

Can you find more?
Try for other areas.

2. HALVING THE BOARD

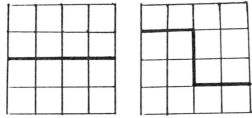

Here are 2 ways of cutting a 4×4 board
into 2 identical pieces:
What other ways are there? Investigate other sizes
of boards.

3. NUMBER CELLS

In this row of cells you start with 3 and 4

3	4			

Then you add 3 and 4 to get 7, then
4 and 7 to get 11, ...

3	4	7	11	18

but if you are given the first and last
numbers only ...

8				52

What are the missing numbers?

For different first and last numbers,
investigate ways of finding the missing
numbers.

Extend to other lengths of cells

4. CUTCAKE

"Cutcake" is a game played by two players, H and V, on a square grid. A rectangle is drawn (of any size). H can cut any piece into smaller pieces by a horizontal line, while V must use a vertical line. When one player cannot move, the other wins. Investigate for different starting rectangles.

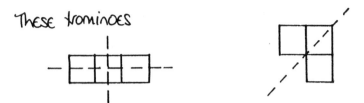

5. TAKING COUNTERS

From a pile of counters 2 players alternately take any number, provided that a) the first player does not take the whole pile b) a player does not take more than twice the last number taken. The player taking the last counter wins. Investigate.

6. POLYOMINOES and SYMMETRY

These trominoes

have respectively 2 axes and 1 axis of symmetry. Investigate when it is possible to devise polyominoes of different numbers of squares with 1, 2, 3, 4, 5, ... lines of symmetry.

7. STRIPS of SQUARES

Strips of squares are made and coloured in two colours.

We call two strips equivalent if they can be reflected or rotated into one another.
How many different strips are there of length five squares?
Investigate this for different strip lengths — different numbers of colours — rings of squares

8. TWO-PIECE TANGRAMS

find some possible ways of rearranging the two pieces of a square shown here.

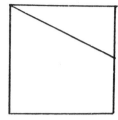

Which of the new shapes generated tessellate on their own?

Make up some other questions about the two piece tangram.
What about other simple tangrams which you can make from, say, equilateral triangles or regular hexagons?

9. PALINDROMIC DATES

The eighteenth of November 1981 has a palindromic date: 18-11-81
(it reads the same backwards as forwards)
When is the next palindromic date?
Which years produce the most palindromic dates?
Which years don't have any?

10. POLYGON SYMMETRIES

Quadrilaterals can have

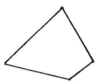

no lines of symmetry

or 1 line

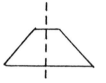

or 2 lines

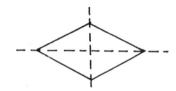

or 4 lines

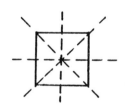

How many lines of symmetry can triangles have? or pentagons? or hexagons? etc?

11. LINES AND REGIONS

Draw 4 straight lines on a piece of plain paper so that you get the maximum number of crossing points. How many crossing points can you get?

How many inside regions are there? outside regions?

Investigate for other numbers of lines.

12. SLICES

What plane shapes can you make by slicing through a cube once?

Try slicing tetrahedrons, octahedrons etc.

13. TESSELLATING HEXIAMONDS

Hexiamonds are shapes made from six equilateral triangles.
Here are some :

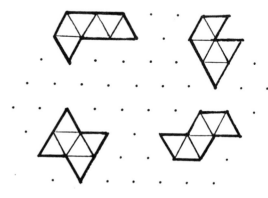

Investigate tessellations of hexiamonds

14. TRANSFORMING NUMBERS

Consider the transformation

$$\frac{a}{b} \rightarrow \frac{a + 2b}{a + b}$$

where a, b are whole numbers.

eg $\frac{1}{1} \rightarrow \frac{3}{2} \rightarrow \frac{7}{5} \rightarrow \frac{17}{12} \rightarrow \cdots$

Investigate transformations of this kind.

15. SPEEDWAY HEATS

In speedway races, there are heats of 4 riders; each rider rides against each other rider exactly once. Devise systems for arranging different totals of riders into heats.

16. MATRIX POWERS

All the numbers here are written in mod 3 (except the powers)

Check that

$$\begin{pmatrix} 2 & 1 \\ 0 & 2 \end{pmatrix}^6 = \begin{pmatrix} 1 & 0 \\ 0 & 1 \end{pmatrix}$$

What is $\begin{pmatrix} 2 & 1 \\ 0 & 2 \end{pmatrix}^7$?

Investigate the powers of other mod 3 matrices.

17. PATIO TILES

Cover this patio with tiles like this

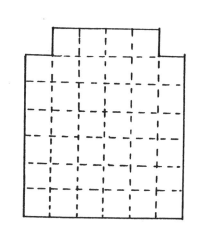

What about this one?

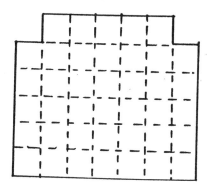

Try other shapes with an area of 40 squares

18. ROUND THE BLOCK

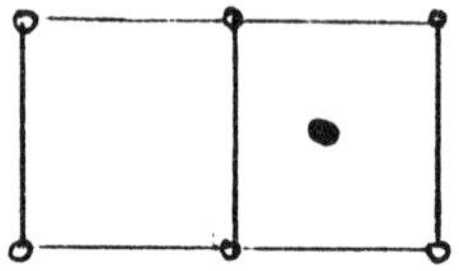

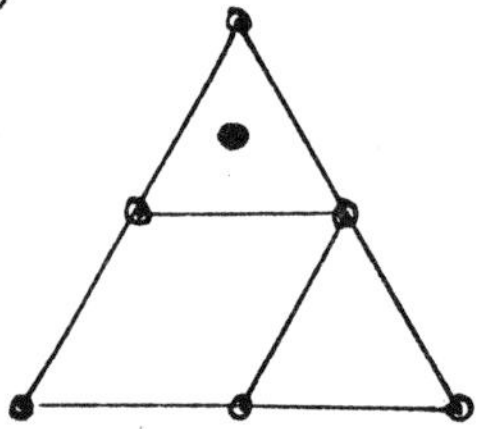

Can you draw a line which starts at the black dot in each network, crosses each branch of that network once and only once, and returns to the black dot?

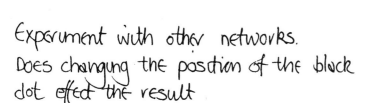

Experiment with other networks.
Does changing the position of the black dot effect the result

19. NEAR TO THE ROOT

"Because 70 is nearer 64 than 81 then $\sqrt{70}$ is nearer 8 than 9"

Test this statement for numbers and their square roots (include some decimals, numbers less than 1 etc)
For which ranges of numbers is this statement not true?

20. CALENDARS

Start with a calendar and investigate

Row Patterns

Diagonal Patterns

Look for Friday 13ths
Investigate how many in different years.

1982

	January	February	March
Mon	4 11 18 25	1 8 15 22	1 8 15 22 29
Tue	5 12 19 26	2 9 16 23	2 9 16 23 30
Wed	6 13 20 27	3 10 17 24	3 10 17 24 31
Thu	7 14 21 28	4 11 18 25	4 11 18 25
Fri	1 8 15 22 29	5 12 19 26	5 12 19 26
Sat	2 9 16 23 30	6 13 20 27	6 13 20 27
Sun	3 10 17 24 31	7 14 21 28	7 14 21 28

	April	May	June
Mon	5 12 19 26	3 10 17 24 31	7 14 21 28
Tue	6 13 20 27	4 11 18 25	1 8 15 22 29
Wed	7 14 21 28	5 12 19 26	2 9 16 23 30
Thu	1 8 15 22 29	6 13 20 27	3 10 17 24
Fri	2 9 16 23 30	7 14 21 28	4 11 18 25
Sat	3 10 17 24	1 8 15 22 29	5 12 19 26
Sun	4 11 18 25	2 9 16 23 30	6 13 20 27

	July	August	September
Mon	5 12 19 26	2 9 16 23 30	6 13 20 27
Tue	6 13 20 27	3 10 17 24 31	7 14 21 28
Wed	7 14 21 28	4 11 18 25	1 8 15 22 29
Thu	1 8 15 22 29	5 12 19 26	2 9 16 23 30
Fri	2 9 16 23 30	6 13 20 27	3 10 17 24
Sat	3 10 17 24 31	7 14 21 28	4 11 18 25
Sun	4 11 18 25	1 8 15 22 29	5 12 19 26

	October	November	December
Mon	4 11 18 25	1 8 15 22 29	6 13 20 27
Tue	5 12 19 26	2 9 16 23 30	7 14 21 28
Wed	6 13 20 27	3 10 17 24	1 8 15 22 29
Thu	7 14 21 28	4 11 18 25	2 9 16 23 30
Fri	1 8 15 22 29	5 12 19 26	3 10 17 24 31
Sat	2 9 16 23 30	6 13 20 27	4 11 18 25
Sun	3 10 17 24 31	7 14 21 28	5 12 19 26

2 months here (May and August) require 6 columns each. What happens in other years?

21. CUBOIDS

We know that it is easy to find cuboids which have the same volume but different surface area. Investigate cuboids which have the same surface area and different volumes.

22. NOUGHTS and CROSSES

Can you devise a strategy for noughts and crosses that will ensure that you
   a) never lose?
   b) always win?

The rules of the game could be changed - for example, the players could be free to play a nought or a cross on each move and the first player to complete a line of three noughts or three crosses would be the winner.

Investigate the consequences of this and other changes in the rules.

23. DRAWING SQUARES

When we attempt to draw these squares in one stroke without going over any line twice we find they are impossible.

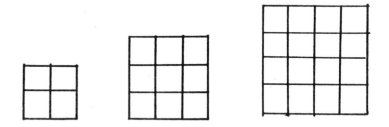

If we try to draw as many of the small squares as we can, we end up with:

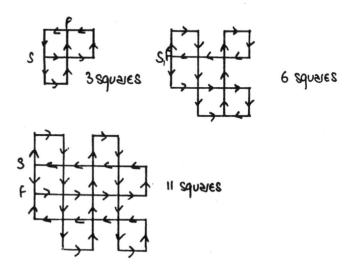

3 squares

6 squares

11 squares

Investigate squares and rectangles in this way

24. QUADRANT TILES

Draw a circle in the middle
of a square.
Colour the corners and
cut into four equal pieces

Each of the four tiles now has an identical
coloured corner. Arrange the four tiles in a
square pattern in any way
you like :-

for example

Repeat the same pattern side by side to
make an overall design.
The pattern must be the same way round,
not reflected or rotated.

Investigate how many different overall
designs are possible.

25. MAXIMUM CONE

A sector is removed from a
10cm radius circle and the
remaining paper is formed
into a cone.

What is the maximum volume the cone
can have?

26. DOTTY SHAPES

Make some shapes with no dots inside.

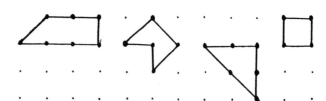

find the area of each shape and the
number of dots on its perimeter.

Do the same for shapes with one dot inside,
and two dots inside, and so on.

27. POLYGONS WITHIN POLYGONS 1

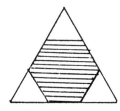

Within the large equilateral triangle is a regular hexagon. How much of the area of the triangle is covered by the hexagon?

Find another hexagon which is only ½ of the area of its surrounding triangle. Investigate similar problems with equilateral triangles in regular hexagons, with squares in regular octagons and so on.

28. POLYGONS WITHIN POLYGONS 2

Find the largest equilateral triangle within a regular hexagon; the largest square within a hexagon ....

Investigate other such problems

Extend to polygons within polyhedra, e.g. find the largest square and regular hexagon within a cube.

29. NUMBER SPIRALS

Investigate the properties of numbers arranged in spirals:

21	22	23	24	25	26
20	7	8	9	10	27
19	6	1	2	11	
18	5	4	3	12	
17	16	15	14	13	

OR

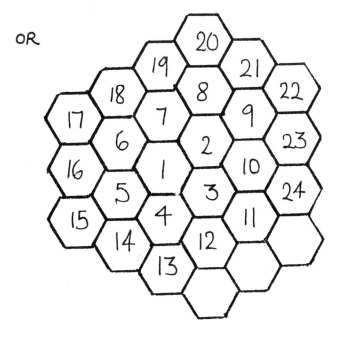

30. TABLES

These are examples of 2 by 2 tables

+	3	5
2	5	7
8	11	13

×	3	8
2	6	16
9	27	72

*	a	b
c	p	q
d	r	s

These are incomplete 2 by 2 tables; can you complete them?

×		
	10	15
	14	21

+	2	3
		30

	7	16
2	7	16
21	21	21

31. HICCUP NUMBERS

Choose a three-digit number, say 327, and repeat it, 327327.
Divide the number by 11; by 13; by 7 - what happens?
Investigate other 'hiccup' numbers and other situations like this.

32. STAMPS

You have got 5p and 7p stamps only. It is possible to post a parcel costing 39p (5+5+5+5+5+7+7 = 39) but you can't put the correct amount on a parcel if it costs 23p.

Make up and investigate problems about stamps and parcels.

What is the biggest parcel that you <u>can't</u> post?

33. MAXIMUM AREA

What is the biggest area that you can enclose with a perimeter of 24cm?

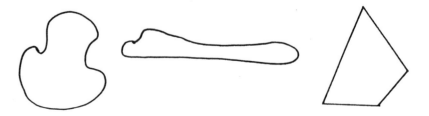

34. JOINING DOTS

An array of dots is joined in pairs:

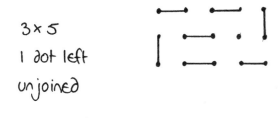

3 × 5
1 dot left
unjoined

4 × 4
4 dots left unjoined

Investigate the maximum number of unjoined dots.

35. ADDING DIGITS

The digits of 122 are 1, 2, 2 and add up to 5. Find all numbers whose digits add up to 5.

Investigate numbers whose digits add up to other totals.

36. MONGE'S SHUFFLE

Monge's method for shuffling cards is as follows: Consider four cards a, b, c, d in that order. b is placed on top of a, then c underneath these two cards, then d on top of these three. For more than four cards, continue in the same way placing alternately on the top then on the bottom. Investigate the effect of successive repetitions of the shuffle.

Devise some other ways of shuffling. Perform a sequence, repeating the shuffle, and investigate the consequences.

37. BREAKING STICKS

A stick is broken into three pieces. When can the pieces make a triangle? What is the probability that this will happen?

If the stick is broken into four pieces, what is the probability that they could make a quadrilateral?

38. MOVING ARROWHEADS

An 'arrowhead' can be made out of counters

```
        •
      •   •
    •   •   •
  •   •   •   •
•   •   •   •   •
```

Its direction can be changed by moving only 5 counters:

```
•   •   •   •   •
  •   •   •   •
    •   •   •
      •   •
        •
```

Investigate puzzles of this kind.

39. AIRLINE LUGGAGE

International Airline Luggage Regulations state:
" Passengers can take any piece of luggage where the sum of the 3 dimensions (length, width, and height) do not exceed 105 ins (or 2.70m)"
Investigate.

40 TESSELLATING PENTOMINOES

Choose a pentomino, say

Turn it through 90° about one corner

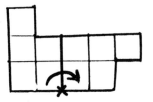

and again, and again

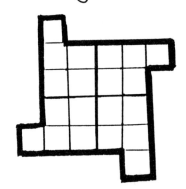

Investigate tessellations of these new shapes

41. PEGBOARD ARRAYS

This is a 7×7 square in a pegboard. A peg is placed in each column, but each time three squares up from the previous peg. [When you get to the top continue counting up from the bottom].

The pegs lie in lines
Investigate.

42. NODES

What topologically different networks can you make with just two 3-nodes or just two 4-nodes? Try for other kinds of nodes.

43. MAXAGON

What is the maximum number of sides a polygon drawn on this grid can have? Investigate for other sizes of grid.

44. PROJECTIONS

Cut out a square from cardboard. View the square from different angles. What shapes can you see?

Investigate views of other cardboard shapes:—
an equilateral triangle
a circle
a cube.

45. AFRICAN NETWORK PATTERNS

Use spotty paper.
These are the first three designs

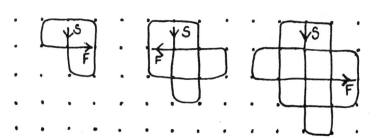

Each is drawn in a continuous movement
Draw these to get the feel of how the
patterns are created.   Draw some bigger
ones.   What is the next size?

Look at
- numbers of squares
- arrangements of squares
- finishing points.

46. CROSSING HEXAGONS

Mark the 6 corners of
a hexagon:

You can get a regular hexagon
if you join them up

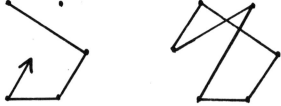

BUT .... if you go round the points
in a different order, you might start
with

This is a crossed hexagon

Investigate crossed polygons

47. FINDING TRIANGLES

Large equilateral triangles are made up from smaller ones. Investigate the numbers of different sized triangles inside.

 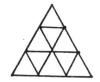 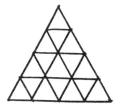

48. PATIENCE

A game of patience is as follows: start with a pack of cards arranged in order. Take the top card and put it on the bottom of the pack, put the second card face up on the table. The third card goes to the bottom of the pack, the fourth on the table. Continue until all cards are on the table. The pack is then turned face downwards and the process is repeated until the cards are back in the original order. Investigate this for different numbers of cards.

49. BABYTAGS

In a hospital, the identification tags of four babies get mixed up.

Two babies were tagged correctly and two wrongly. How many ways could this happen?

In how many different ways can they all be labelled wrongly?

In how many ways three be wrong and one correct?

Three correct and one wrong?

Investigate problems like this for different numbers of babies.

50. SQUARING MATRICES

Find matrices (2 by 2 to start with) so that when you square them, you get the same result as when you square each element

eg $\begin{pmatrix} 2 & 5 \\ 0 & 3 \end{pmatrix}^2 = \begin{pmatrix} 4 & 25 \\ 0 & 9 \end{pmatrix} = \begin{pmatrix} 2^2 & 5^2 \\ 0^2 & 3^2 \end{pmatrix}$

51. BROOM and BAND

You are given a wide rubber band and a broom handle. Wind the rubber band around the broom so that it lies flat, without twists. (It will, of course, cross itself)

Investigate the number of turns that can be made.

Extend to a Möbius band.

52. ISOMETRIC TRANSFORMATIONS

Instead of the usual square grid use an isometric grid:

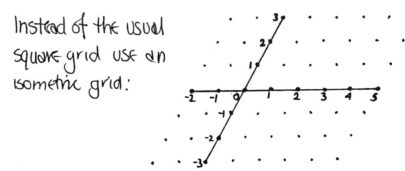

What transformation has the matrix $\begin{pmatrix} 1 & 1 \\ 0 & -1 \end{pmatrix}$?

Investigate other transformations and their matrices.

53. MOD 5 TRANSFORMATIONS

A grid is made with axes labelled 0 to 4.
Investigate the transformations produced by matrices such as
$\begin{pmatrix} 2 & 0 \\ 0 & 2 \end{pmatrix}$, $\begin{pmatrix} 1 & 0 \\ 0 & 2 \end{pmatrix}$ where all numbers are written mod 5.

54. BELL RINGING

In bell ringing with three bells, there are six different orders in which they can be rung eg $(1,2,3)$, $(2,3,1)$ etc.
The aim is to produce all six orders before repeating one of them. No bell is allowed to move up or down more than one place from one order to the next (so $(1,2,3)$ cannot be followed by $(2,3,1)$)
Investigate.

55. BINARY ONES

If we change numbers to base two, we get
$$1 \rightarrow 1, \quad 2 \rightarrow 10, \quad 3 \rightarrow 11, \quad 4 \rightarrow 100$$
$$5 \rightarrow 101, \ldots\ldots$$

If we classify these binary numbers into sets according to how many ones, we get
$$S_1 = \{1, 2, 4, 8, \ldots\}$$
$$S_2 = \{3, 5, 6, 9, \ldots\}$$
$$S_3 = \{7, 11, 13, \ldots\}$$
$$S_4 = \{15, \ldots\}$$

Investigate.

56. ELEPHANT WALK

An elephant, very fond of buns, walks through a set of cages each containing one bun.

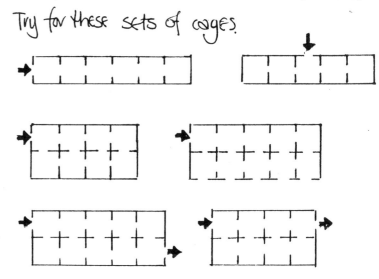

To get all of the buns the elephant must walk through a minimum of 7 cages.
(there and back)

Try for these sets of cages.

Investigate for different sets of cages with entrances and exits in various places.

57. FROGS

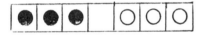

Try to swap the black and white counters round (▢⟨o⟩⟨o⟩⟨o⟩⟨●⟩⟨●⟩⟨●⟩) by either sliding a counter into an empty square (⟨●⟩⟨●⟩⟨●⟩←▢⟨o⟩⟨o⟩) or jumping over <u>one</u> other counter into an empty square (⟨●⟩⟨●⟩⟨●⟩▢⟨o⟩⟨o⟩).
What is the minimum number of moves required?
Investigate for other numbers of counters.

58. FOLDING STAMPS

Six postage stamps are in a block. How many different ways are there of folding them into one pile?

59. ENCLOSURES

The diagram shows how 7 yellow (5cm) Colour Factor rods can be used to enclose an area of 28 cm².

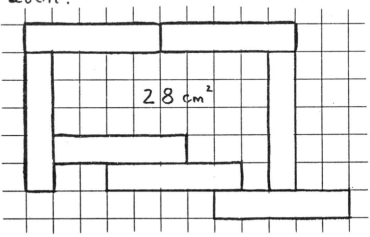

28 cm²

What is the maximum area that could be enclosed with these rods?
(Note: The edges of the rods must lie along the lines on the centimetre square paper and joints like this are not permitted.

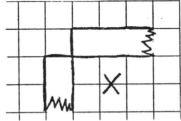

Investigate for different colours (lengths) and different numbers of rods —
eg. the maximum area enclosed by 4 crimson (8cm) rods.

60. DOTTY VARIATIONS

How many equilateral triangles are there on this grid?

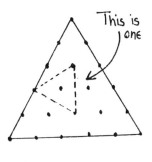

This is one

Repeat for other size triangle grids (eg 6×6)

How many equilateral triangles on various sizes of hexagon grids?

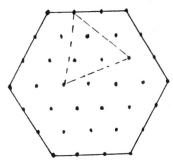

How many hexagons (regular) are there on various sizes of hexagon grids?

How many parallelograms are there on this grid?

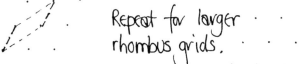

Repeat for larger rhombus grids.

61. TRANSFORMING TRIANGLES

Which triangles can the shaded triangle land on exactly after one translation?

one rotation?

one reflection?

Try the same problems for these diagrams.

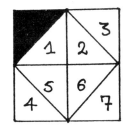

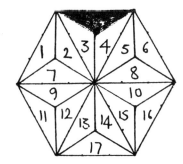

<u>Other Titles in the ATM Activity Series Include:</u>

Points of Departure 1
A collection of 75 starting points for
mathematical investigations suitable for varying
ages and abilities.

Mathematical Activities From Poland
A collection of imaginative activities for older
primary school children.

**Problem Solving Workcards For Use With
Microcomputers**
A collection of worksheets of mathematical
activities for children using inexpensive
computers with BASIC (ZX81, SPECTRUM, BBC)

Sticks
A collection of ideas and starting points for the
primary and secondary classrom based on the use
of applicator and other similar sticks.

Pegboards
Activities for children of all ages.

Fifteen Starters for the Secondary Classroom
As the title implies.

Pegboard Games
Pegboard games with suggestions and encouragement
for further development.

Geoboards
A collection of ideas and starting points for the
primary and secondary classroom.

Rods, Blocks and Balances
A workbook for teachers of 8 - 13 year olds using
coloured rods, interlocking cubes and equalisers.

Numbers Everywhere
Number situations for the secondary classroom.

Turning the Tables
Number situations for the primary or lower
secondary classroom.

These Have Worked For Us
Some 'starters', 'occupiers' or 'mini-projects'.
Also for the least able?

These and other ATM publications are available from ATM Office, Kings Chambers, Queen Street, Derby, DE1 3DA
Please refer to the current publications list/order form for price details.